3 4 5
9 10

Published by Scholastic Inc.,
90 Old Sherman Turnpike, Danbury, Connecticut 06816.

SCHOLASTIC and associated logos are trademarks
and/or registered trademarks of Scholastic Inc.

ISBN 0-7172-8608-8

Printed in the U.S.A.

First Scholastic Printing, August 2005

My  Book

by Jane Belk Moncure
illustrated by Ben Mahan

SCHOLASTIC INC.

New York Toronto London Auckland Sydney
Mexico City New Delhi Hong Kong Buenos Aires

This is Little one.

Little  lives in . . .

the house of one.

The house of one has one room.

He sits at one table.
He drinks one glass
of milk. He eats one
bowl of soup . . .

one slice of cake and one apple.

Each day Little  goes for a walk.

He hops one hop. Can you?

He jumps one jump.
Can you?

He smells one little flower.
Can you?

One day he finds . . .

one tree and
one acorn.

He gives the acorn to one squirrel.

Then Little one finds
one unicorn.

He claps one clap. Can you?

Little  one finds one wagon.

"The unicorn can pull my wagon," he says.

Little one finds . . .

one mouse.

"Come, ride in my wagon," he says.
The mouse squeaks one squeak. Can you?

Next he finds . . .

one kitten.

The kitten is sad.
"Come, ride in my wagon," says Little one.

One mouse jumps out.

How many kittens jump in?

Now Little  finds . . .

one puppy.

The puppy is sad.

"Come, ride in my wagon," says Little

How many kittens jump out?

How many puppies jump in?

One happy puppy barks one little bark.
Can you?

Then Little  sees . . .

one  star in the sky.

"We must go home," he says.

Away they go.

Little  gives the unicorn one
pat on the head . . .

and one bucket of corn.

He gives the puppy
one bone . . .

and one hug.

He eats one peanut butter and jelly sandwich . . .

And drinks one cup of hot cocoa.

Little 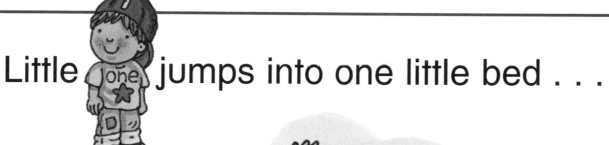 jumps into one little bed . . .

with one big jump. Can you?

He pulls up
one blanket,

winks one wink,

turns off one light,

and says, "Good night." Can you?

Little  finds one of everything.

one flower

one wagon

one tree

one mouse

one acorn

one kitten

one squirrel

one puppy

one star

Now you find one thing.

"See what I can do," says Little 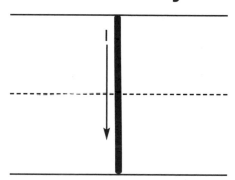 one.
He makes a I this way.

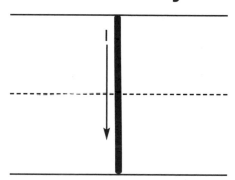

Then he makes the number word like this:

You can make them in the air with your finger.

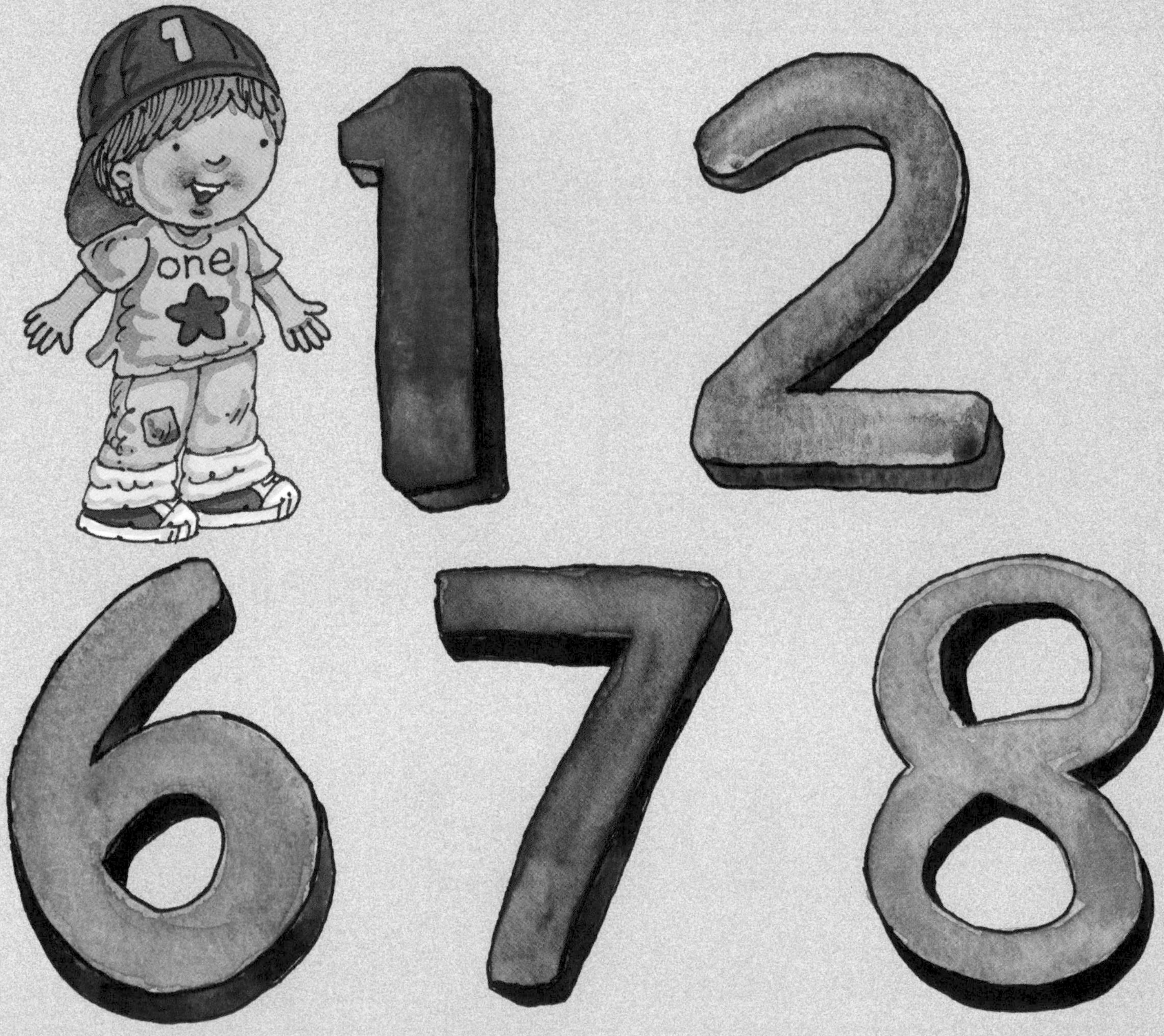
1
one
1
2
6
7
8